Dedication

To my three sons, Seth, Levi and Matt, to whom I spent years reading bedtime stories and decades later, inspired me to write as a result of their drive and motivation.

Where is My Tablet?

SECOND EDITION

By Rose-Edith Morgan, M.S.   Illustrations By Sabrina Fajardo

Hello friends! My name is Donna. I live in 4 houses...That's right, four houses. Most of my friends live in one or two. I live in four. I have my Mom's house, my Dad's house, my Auntie's house and my Grandma's house.

I have my own bedroom in all four of my houses. My Auntie's house has a big staircase. I love to run up and down the stairs. My Grandma's house has a big area of plants in front that I call the forest. Well, actually it's like a baby forest.

I love going to my Grandma's house. Some days, she picks me up at school. I love seeing her red car. My Grandma lets me listen to my favorite music in her car! I always do my homework in my bedroom, after my snack.

When I get home from school, I am hungry. Grandma always has a healthy snack ready for me. Most of the time, I have fresh strawberries, grapes, kiwis, and bananas. Sometimes I have a mango if it is in season. Grandma says, "We should eat healthy foods to grow and be strong."

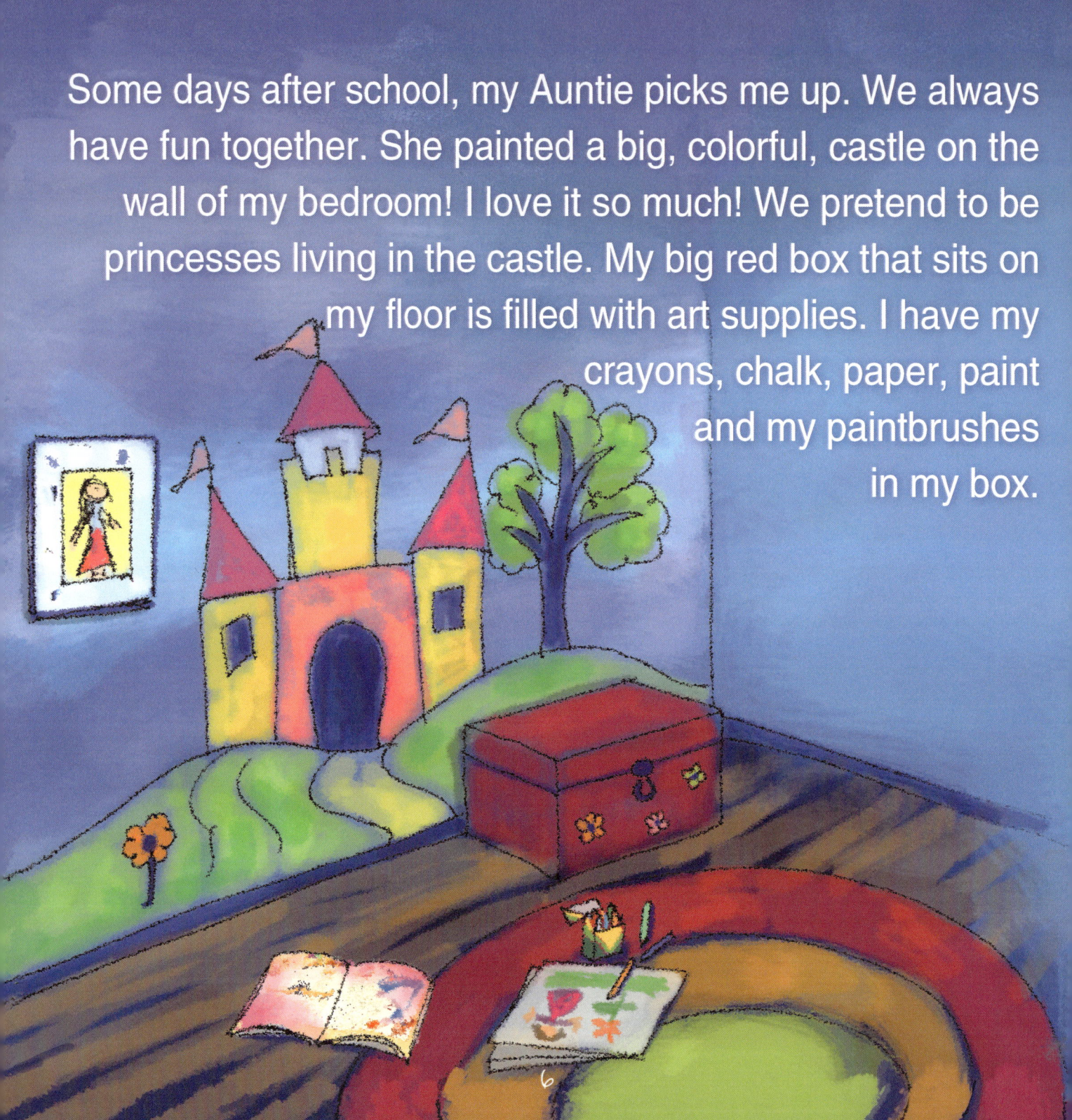

Some days after school, my Auntie picks me up. We always have fun together. She painted a big, colorful, castle on the wall of my bedroom! I love it so much! We pretend to be princesses living in the castle. My big red box that sits on my floor is filled with art supplies. I have my crayons, chalk, paper, paint and my paintbrushes in my box.

On the other wall in my room, my name is painted in big, sparkly, pink letters. There are yellow stars all around my name. Seeing my name makes me feel so special. Sometimes I love to sit on my bed, hold my pillow with the big red heart and look at my name.

I love all of my houses. At my Mom's house, I love my bed that has drawers underneath. I keep my books and some of my toys in those drawers. At my Dad's house, I have green walls, a purple bedspread and a purple lampshade. Even my rug has lots of bright stripes!

I am lucky because I have my own room in each house. At my Auntie's house, my room makes me feel like I am a princess. At Grandma's house, I love the picture of me hanging in my room. My Auntie painted that picture. My bookshelf has some of my favorite books that Grandma and I read together. All of the rooms are different and are filled with things I love.

In my Mommy's house, I have a big dollhouse. It has rooms with furniture, and it even has a mirror. My dolls have so many clothes. When my friends come over, we love to play with the dollhouse.

In my Daddy's house, my bedroom has my favorite stuffed animals, Louie and Alexa. They are my soft, cozy panda bears. My Daddy bought them when we went to the zoo.

I have my very own tablet! My Mommy gave it to me for my birthday. I can take it with me wherever I go. Sometimes Grandma and I watch movies on it. Other times we play games on it.

I have my favorite board games at my Grandma's house. I love when Grandma and I play games. Grandma always says "We play fair and square." Sometimes I win and sometimes I lose. I don't like losing, but I know I can't always win. Sometimes Grandma tells me stories about when she was a little girl.

I love to draw. At my Auntie's house, we draw together. She teaches me about many famous artists. My Auntie always hangs my pictures on her refrigerator. She is very proud of my drawings.

Most of the time, I live in my Mommy's house. I have a big calendar on the wall. My Mom writes on the calendar who picks me up from school each day. When my Grandma picks me up, I usually have dinner at her house. She makes a funny face on my dinner plate, with all of the food. She also gives me apple juice, my favorite drink, for dinner.

When I go to my Auntie's house, after I finish my homework, we bake together. Cupcakes are my favorite dessert. I always get to select my favorite flavors to bake. My very favorite flavor is pistachio.

I love my four houses, but one thing really bothers me. Sometimes I forget if I left my tablet at my Dad's house, or my Grandma's house. Did I leave it at my Mommy's house, or my Auntie's house? Then I get upset if I can't find it.

I do so many things on my tablet. I play games and watch videos. My Mommy helps me with my Spelling words on my tablet. "Tablet" was one of my Spelling words this week! Of my ten Spelling words, that one was my favorite!

My Daddy speaks Spanish and Italian. He teaches me words in both languages on my tablet. Then he shows me different countries on a map on my tablet. I am learning about Italy.

My Auntie and I look for new cupcake recipes on my tablet. We find so many for all of the different flavors. I am learning all about kitchen tools, ingredients for cupcakes, icing and baking temperatures.

Sometimes I think I packed my tablet in my yellow backpack, but then I don't have it when I want it. That makes me feel sad. My Mommy says when there is a problem, there is always a solution. We started to think of solutions.

I love my backpack. It is yellow with a big red and purple flower on it. Mommy and I thought of a few solutions to my problem. We came up with the BEST solution...A PURPLE RIBBON!! Mommy tied a big purple ribbon on my backpack. When I see it, it will remind me to get my tablet.

When I am rushing to leave and going to get my backpack, I now know to get my tablet because I see the purple ribbon. Sometimes if my backpack is too full, I can put the tablet in the smaller compartment.

I am so lucky. I have a big family who loves me. I feel at home and am so happy in my four houses.

Thanks to my Mommy, I never worry about leaving my tablet in another house.
She and I came up with a solution.

The Purple Ribbon worked for me.
It taught me to always try to come up with the best solution to a problem.

Copyright © 2016 Rose-Edith Morgan

All rights reserved. This book or any portion thereof may not be reproduced or used in any manner whatsoever without the express written permission of the publisher except for the use of brief quotations in a book review.

Where is My Tablet?
Updated Second Edition, 2024

Rose-Edith Morgan

www.ingramcontent.com/pod-product-compliance
Lightning Source LLC
LaVergne TN
LVRC091354060526
838201LV00042B/417